# The Story of Moulton Windmill

from 1822 to 1998
and of the families who owned and operated it.
The tallest working windmill in Great Britain
as told by John Biggadike, the last Miller of Moulton to
Jim Critchley and Peter Hall

Published 2014 by Moulton Windmill, Moulton, Lincs

ISBN   978-0-9930741-0-3

# Foreword

Some five years ago, I was approached by Jim Critchley who had overheard me talking about my years at the mill and further back into the past. He expressed the opinion that my memories should be preserved and said that he would help me write a book, to which I readily agreed.

Following Jim's untimely death, Peter Hall volunteered to take over and at last we have completed the task.

Moulton Mill has always been at the centre of my life, playing there as a child with no thoughts of any other occupation other than following my father and grandfather in the business of Miller and Corn Merchant, never thinking that the days of the village miller, and of the small farmers who provided the backbone of the business, were numbered.

The mill was only ever owned by two families, the Kings and my own, both operating the mill for seventy years each, with the remaining thirty years between by A. W. Tindall as a tenant.

I hope readers enjoy this account of the changing times recorded.

John Biggadike, Moulton, October 2014

*John Biggadike*

*With Best Wishes*

*Dec 13 2014*

3

# Preface

This book is the result of a partnership between three men. John Biggadike III retired as the last miller in Moulton, Lincolnshire in 1995. He still lives in the village.

Jim Critchley was a volunteer Guide at Moulton Windmill who was determined to capture and document the history of the mill. Tragically, Jim died suddenly on 21st November 2012.

Jim decided that the most effective way to achieve his goal was to sit with John and capture all the history, stories and anecdotes that John had stored up over his life. This he did. The two men met regularly and frequently over a number of years. John talked, Jim listened, scribbled and asked questions.

The story telling was supplemented by painstaking research as Jim sought out documentation in libraries, the Lincolnshire Archives, censuses, private collections and the Spalding Gentlemen's Society.

As John says in his Foreword, the Mill was only ever owned by two families, and operated by three during its commercial life. This book is the story of those families, their lives in Moulton and surrounding villages, and factors that finally drove the Mill out of business.

Following Jim's untimely death, I volunteered to review the papers he had collected and finish the book he had started, and so became the third man of the partnership. It has been a real pleasure to do so.

Peter Hall, Spalding, October 2014

# History

When the district between the Welland and the Nene Rivers was first settled, it was difficult to find dry areas, except for a ridge of silt land roughly parallel with the coast.

The Romans built a sea bank stretching from Wainfleet to the River Nene, a distance of fifty miles. The Roman Bank and Mill Marsh Road in Moulton Seas End are part of this bank. There used to be a slight hump in Common Road near Bank House Farm where the sea barrier was for some time. The new sea bank was built by a few of the local farmers after World War II. Up to that time the sea bank was at the T-junction at the end of Red Cow Drove by the old pub called the Hare the Hounds.

The Romans introduced the cultivation of corn into the fens, as this area was one of the most productive areas in the Empire. The grain was exported to Europe, mainly through the port of Wainfleet (Vainona) as it was the first sheltered land after the boats left the North Sea.

Settlements were built by the Anglo Saxons, which they named 'ton', taking the leader's name ('Weston') or what seems likely in the case of Moulton, the town with a mill – 'Muilton'. These villages were situated on the higher ground where they grew considerable amounts of grain with cattle in the town lands, the land near to the village. The art of evaporating salt from the sea by using salt pans would have been a useful source of income or trade. They built wattle huts on the highest land and where the church is now was probably the nucleus of the Anglo Saxon village.

The fens were a vast morass below the height of the sea level and liable to flood at each high tide; a place of meres and pools, mists and moisture laden air. The inhabitants were a hardy, amphibious race hardened by their struggle to maintain their life style against the sea and rivers, living in wattle and daube huts on whatever dry land they could find.

When finally drawn, the parish boundaries were elongated rectangles of land with a narrow sea frontage and a long narrow strip stretching inland. The further these areas reached inland the greater the threat from inland flooding as a result of drainage from the Midlands. A sea bank would have protected the parish from the spring tides and silt gradually raised the land, further protecting the village with extra dry land. It would have taken about ten years before the new land became suitable for grazing; a new bank would then be built further out into what used to be the sea bed and the process would continue.

The locals could differentiate between the qualities of each area of land, whereas visitors would have thought it all the same. The quality of the land in the area is highly variable, with some poor fields being heavy clay while the best are fine silt. This is a situation that has lasted through the drainage schemes that were completed in the nineteenth century. Local farmers have, and have always had, a different view of the fens since they know their land intimately and have always had an abundance of grazing lands and fertile fields which are rich: in fish, fowl, sedge for thatching and fuel, as well as areas of sea marsh for sheep pasture.

There is a record of a discussion between the prior of Spalding Monastery and the vicar of Moulton in about 1230, concerning the distribution of mill tithes. It was said that the parish of Moulton had five mills and it was decided that they should be divided by granting the tithes from two of the mills to the vicar of Moulton and the other three to the prior of Spalding[1].

On New Year's Day 1287 the whole of South Holland was turned into a standing pool with many people being drowned. Such drainage that existed then was by means of the rivers and remains of the Roman systems. The land north of Ravens Bank was drained by the Moulton, Whaplode and Holbeach rivers. It was the responsibility of landowners to repair their length of sea bank but not much was achieved except for the lands maintained by the religious houses such as Moulton and Spalding, which kept the drains in good order. As a consequence they had small enclosures of arable land.

During the reign of Queen Elizabeth I another flood occurred ,during which villages were lost and the whole area flooded. Ships were destroyed with one being driven onto the roof of a house, its sailors clinging to the roof.

During this period many complaints were made to the monarch, concerning the loss of land and goods, as well as the destruction of the sea banks. Not much attention was given to the problem until the reign of James I, when large-scale draining of the Deeping Fen was undertaken.

The resources of South Holland could support a larger population than elsewhere in Lincolnshire. In 1563, on

---

1        British Library Coles M. S. 43, additional manuscript 5827  020 7412 7513

average, there would have been between 11 and 21 families living on a thousand acres. There were six good sized market towns in the area each with about 150 families, Spalding having 154 families and Holbeach 147.

There were markets in Holbeach and Spalding, which were kept this distance apart (a return journey of 12 miles) as a horse and cart would be expected to travel it in a day

Travellers going to Norfolk from Lincolnshire would gather at Long Sutton ready to make the dangerous journey across the fens. Their guides were likely to have come from Terrington or Walpole St. Andrews as there were men there who would be familiar with the area.

The King family were yeoman farmers having lived in the parish for many years. In the Moulton Church register of 1600 there is an entry showing that Thomas King married Margaret Witt. The eldest sons were named Thomas until 1737 when the third son, Robert, inherited, resulting for the next generations that the eldest sons were named Robert.

The Grundy map of 1730 at the Gentlemen's Society in Spalding shows a possible drainage mill on Moulton Mere Drain, at its junction with the High Road on the boundary between the Weston and Moulton parishes.

Did the Kings own this mill and did they move it across the road, converting it to a grinding mill? Was it the same mill as advertised for sale in 1828 but without a fantail shown in the details? Fantails were invented in 1745 by Edward Lee so if the smock mill had been built as new, after that date, then surely it would have included a fantail? The Mill (Elloe Mill) was situated on the track known as Elloe Lane.

Moulton Marsh at this time was a wide expanse of marshy land, drained by the Moulton River and stretching as far as Bicker. The usable road was gradually becoming wider and wider as vehicles, travelling towards either Holbeach or Spalding, tried to avoid the worst track and went where they could. There are stories of vehicles becoming lost among this morass of deep ruts, potholes or ponds while travelling wide of the original road.

Spalding Gate, where the Elloe Stone is situated, was in ancient times among the main roads across the county before the High Road was created.

This was the age of road improvement. In the more important parts of the country these new roads used Macadam's methods ,but here in the fens cheaper methods were used for the road between Spalding and Holbeach, which was made into a turnpike (toll road) in 1746.

Arthur Youngs's book 'General view of the agriculture of the county of Lincoln', published in 1813 and written whilst the first Fosdyke bridge was under construction, describes the journey he took from Wisbech to Boston along the future A17. He described the turnpike road as "generally made with silt or sea sand, when moderately wet is very good, dusty in fine weather, heavy in wet, and set like mortar after a thaw. Take the county in general and they are below par."

# Enclosure Act – brief explanation

The Enclosure Acts were a series of Acts of Parliament which enclosed fields and common land in the country. They removed previously existing rights of local people to carry out activities in these areas, such as cultivation, cutting hay, grazing animals or using other resources such as small timber, fish, and turf.

Enclosure Acts for small areas had been passed sporadically since the 12th century but the majority were passed between 1750 and 1860. Much larger areas were also enclosed during this time and in 1801 the Enclosure (Consolidation) Act was passed to tidy up previous acts. In 1845 another General Enclosure Act allowed for the appointment of Enclosure Commissioners who could enclose land without submitting a request to Parliament.

Under this process there were over 5,000 individual Enclosure Acts and 21% of land in England was enclosed, amounting to nearly 11,000 square miles.

# The Kings

In the Enclosure Act Robert King I obtained two sites, one on the High Road containing a mill with a second next to the church where the present tower mill stands.

On the site owned by the Kings on the High Road they built a house with crenellated walls and Gothic shaped windows. This was demolished in 2007 with a provision in the planning permission that the owner's plaque from the old house be transferred to the new house. Hence the plaque on the front of the house 'R. E. K.'. I believe the date stone which has been lost showed the date of 1800.

The Kings operated their mill from here, along an unmade road behind Gothic House, until it was advertised for sale in 1828.

In 1780 the King family had a plot on Moulton High Street, held from St. John's College, Cambridge. St John's owns large tracts of land throughout England including some in Weston, Whaplode and Moulton.

When the builders of the care home behind the mill, were clearing the site they came across what might have been the marks of a mill underneath the grass. In order to achieve firm foundations piling was necessary before building could commence.

The mill house and bake house were built late in the eighteenth century and were originally thatched, but later were slated. There is little firm evidence that a mill existed on the site before the present mill, but in the Burgess print of 1797, there is a loaded horse and waggon shown in the drawing travelling in the direction of the present mill.

The King family had made their money earlier and were therefore able to spend a lot on building Moulton Mill. They built the finest and tallest windmill I have ever been in. Although it was mine I am not saying it for that reason but because they had not stinted on the cost. They built it tall and high on this flat land. The taller a mill is, the greater is its ability to catch the wind where a shorter mill couldn't. Robert King III built this fine mill and owned it until his death in 1863.

The building of Moulton Mill was started in 1822, and it took about six years to construct, although this date is not set in stone. When building in the first quarter of the nineteenth century, in order to lift bricks and other materials up the mill the lifting would have been done by human labour or using a block and tackle powered by horses and oxen. The main shaft and the stones would have been lifted using blocks and tackles mounted from tripods placed on the floors above which the items were to be mounted. They would have been pulled up using the muscles of men or horses.

All of the ceiling beams have scratch moulded edges, turned newel posts and there is a miller's office - the only one in the country. The spur wheel and stone nuts at Moulton Mill are unusual. In most mills they have an iron-toothed spur wheel and wood stone nuts. This is reversed at Moulton as it has wooden spur wheel teeth and metal stone nuts, making the mill quieter to run.

After the tower mill was working, the smock mill on the High

Road was advertised for sale on condition it was removed at least ten miles from Moulton to avoid competition with the newly built mill. It didn't sell and was advertised again a year later.

The oldest graffiti in the mill dates from this time, shortly after it had been built. Under the staircase that is in the upper granary room is "Charles Merriman came to the mill in 1847/8/9/50". He must have been one of the first millers, working here for four years until he left to better himself. He took over Hunley Mill in Weston Hills, which was demolished in the 1920s. Incidentally, part of the oak timber from Hunley Mill was used to construct the cupboards, in the strong room, at Spalding Gentleman's Society. (A picture of Hunley Mill is shown in the photographs.)

A timeline for the King family is given below:-

In 1813 Robert III (the builder of Moulton Mill) married Elizabeth Diggle, a daughter of Edward Diggle, the owner of Gedney Hill Mill. He had a large family of five daughters, some of whom died young, and two sons, one of whom, Robert, died at the age of sixteen. The second son, James Measure King, inherited upon the death of his father. After Elizabeth's death in 1839, in her thirties, Robert III married Mary Marshall and there were two children Robert and Edward George. Robert became a wealthy Harley Street physician, returning to Moulton on his retirement to live in Boyfield House. His brother Edward George was a Doctor of Divinity and entered the priesthood, becoming Rector of Gayton in Northamptonshire.

In 1861 James Measure King (1821-1879), the second son of Robert King III was at the time a miller, baker and farmer. He married Mary Cowley (1820-1904) living in the Mill House and Selling House with his wife. Robert King III, the miller, was living in Mulberry House next door. On his father's death in 1868, James, having been in partnership with his father for some years, inherited the property, spending most of his time as the miller, to the extent that he became known as "Miller King".

The King Family Tree is shown in Appendix 1.

Robert King, the physician, had two children, Robert (1874 -1914) and Margaret, who never married. Captain Robert King, (the son), who died in action in the Great War and whose name is on both the parish and grammar school war memorials in the church, had two children but both died while still young.

Arthur Cowley King (1855-1923) inherited on the death of his father James in September 1879, and married Maria Webster (1853-1937). He must have continued milling as well as farming for about ten years, before renting out the mill in 1889. He lived in Mill House whilst his mother lived in Mulberry House. He later moved into Wisteria House, opposite the present doctors' surgery. Wisteria House was demolished when the road was widened to improve the junction with West Cobgate, then a narrow road.

Claude King who was the eldest son of Arthur Cowley King, lived in Mulberry House with his mother and three unmarried sisters. He inherited the premises in 1923 and never married, but there was always one of the girls at home to take care of him. They were gentle folk who took afternoon tea on the lawn with Claude who was very much a gentleman of the old school and he never did manual work.

When Claude died in 1949, the farmland had already gone, so what was left of the estate was sold and split among the family of three surviving sisters and a brother, Les, who was a fields-man for a flax growing company in north Lincolnshire. At the auction of the property in 1951 the mill and Mill House and were sold to Mr. J. T. Biggadike Junior for £2,800. Mulberry House and the Bake House were sold separately from the mill.

# Mr. A.W. Tindall

In 1889, the King family made the decision to rent out the mill, the Bake House having been rented separately earlier.

A.W. Tindall took Moulton Mill, in 1889, when he was a relatively young man of about 27. He was a year and a day younger than my grandfather. Mr. Tindall married and lived in Moulton where he ran a big farm as well as his milling business.

Arthur Tindall lived in at least two of the larger village houses. He rented The Goddards in 1891, living there with his wife before he moved to the Manor House next to the Church. Manor House was the farmhouse and the farmyard and buildings were alongside on Bell Lane. He progressed as a flour miller, then began merchanting, whilst my grandfather was always a provender miller of animal feed and merchanting grain.

Soon after Mr. Tindall arrived at the mill, a programme of modernisation commenced. One part of this was to install a large steam engine. This engine required a tremendous amount of water, so a huge well was dug in the mill yard and a cistern to catch the rainwater from the mill was installed, with pipes taking the water to the engine.

As well as the purchase and installation of a steam engine, a drive was installed going through the mill basement and into the mill, then going vertically through the mill floors to the great spur wheel. Up to the point of this drive being put in, the mill basement would have been empty. There would have not been a need for a basement except for ensuring that the carts that were delivering grist, would be able to move sacks from the carts straight into the mill on a level surface, by the use of sack trucks. This vertical shaft was necessary to turn the Wallower and thus operate the sack hoist.

The engine that was running the stones could have run all day, or whenever the stones were needed to grind. As it was a big mill which had a steam engine to supply power, it didn't warrant the expense of putting the sails back after they came off in the storm of December 1894. Tindall himself was only a tenant and the Kings would not have wanted the expense of restoring the sails. When he needed to grind animal feed, he would have used the engine and the mill stones on the first floor.

He also improved the already-present store behind the mill, increasing it from one to two storeys with a tall upper floor to accommodate the machinery for his flour plant. Here he put in a two sack (40 stone, five hundredweight, 254kg) per hour flour plant with rollers and screens, purchased from Turners of Ipswich, to sieve out the flour and bran.

It is not known who paid for the installation of the flour plant. However, it is known that Tindall's rent was only £35 per half year and from a landlord's point of view this would be insufficient to justify the investment required for the installation of the flour plant. Certainly, Arthur Tindall was reimbursed for any repairs to the mill as a receipt book records that 15/- was paid to A. Tindall for repairs to the office window, £13 for stable windows and £13 for insurance.

Following Tindall's modernisation work, the granary building was almost full of machinery, with little room to move around. The bins at the top of the mill fed this plant which meant that many 18 stone (114 kg) sacks of wheat had to be lifted the height of the mill, before passing through the mill wall on floor 2 to the flour machinery. The heavy rollers were on the ground floor with the screening and sieving plant, whilst the elevators that fed this machinery went right down into the basement. In 1950, the long wooden elevators were quickly sold off by the King family as farmers were beginning to put dryers onto their farms and they would have found them useful. The machinery was left in situ in the Kings' lifetime and was not removed as scrap metal with other pieces inside the mill until after the Claude King's death. Some of his machinery remains around the mill.

On the night of 21st/22nd December 1894, there was a violent storm. The wind got behind the sails of the windmill and they were severely damaged, to the extent that they were no longer complete and the remains had to be removed. One of Tindall's granddaughters came to visit me and she said that her mother was born a few days before that night. It must have been an exciting night, the weather producing a really fierce storm in which many ships were lost and many mills damaged. One of Arthur Cowley King's daughters said that her father was running around the village in his night gown telling everyone that the sails had come off. Mary Slater tells that her grandfather left the Axe and Handsaw pub and returned home saying that the sails had come off the mill.

An extract from West Elloe Deanery Magazine dated January

1895 states:

"Moulton

The gale which burst upon the country with such sudden violence during the night of Friday December 21st caused serious damage. The sails of our village Mill, of which we are all so proud, as a beautiful example of its class, were ruthlessly hurled down through the fury of the blast, and completely wrecked, to say nothing of the general damage inflicted by the process to the upper portions of the mill and to the buildings at its base."

In 1908 one of the Holbeach mills, situated beside the railway station, became available and Tindall bought it. The nearness of the railway station was useful to him to help with the movement of grain and flour. He moved the business straight away creating a very large business, selling flour to all parts of the country using both the railway and his own lorries. In my time it was 'A. W. Tindall Ltd.' and so remained until the 1970's, but he still owned the farm in Moulton as well as keeping the lease on Moulton Mill, which didn't run out until 1921. He didn't move out of the mill and house until the lease ran out. As soon as the Holbeach enterprise was established he only made limited use of Moulton Mill but he kept his workman living in the house. Then Moulton Mill was leased to Leslie King who together with his brother Claude was the miller for the next three years.

The field next to the Mill which was owned by St John's College Cambridge, was let to Tindall as his grass field where he grazed his mill horses. Tindall moved into Holbeach and lived in Barrington House next to his new business. As he had no sons, but five daughters, he eventually brought in, Mr. J.W. Bennett from a milling family in Downham Market as a Director. Tindall's family became directors as did members of Mr. Bennett's. Later the company run by Mr. Bennett was built into what would be called a conglomerate, after taking over Birch's Mill in Spalding and Turner Brothers' Mill in Pinchbeck. Mr. Tindall moved from Holbeach to Hunstanton and left the other directors to the day-to-day running of his company but he would get his chauffeur to drive him, into Holbeach to check on the business. Occasionally he would attend Spalding Corn Exchange where I remember meeting him a very few times. By this time his Moulton farm had been let to tenant farmers and the family may still own part of the farm through a family trust.

The first clerk, started on the desk at Moulton windmill, was a Moulton Grammar School boy. He remained with the firm for all of his working life and his signature 'F. K. Kingerley, 1912', when he would have been aged 16, occurs on one of the bins near the top of the mill, (to the left of the bin that has been renovated and roughly at eye height). He became a director of the company and was later joined by Peter Lown who was another Moulton Grammar School pupil and a contemporary of mine, who also became a Director, living in his home town of Holbeach.

The photograph showing the mill and a group of people in front of the Bake House shows W. Webb, the miller, and Charlie Hull who worked there. Mrs Bell, whose husband was a plumber, is in the photograph, but had no connection with the mill. There is a man deep in the shadows and another near the mill. The chimney seems out of proportion because it is nearer to the camera than the Mill. The windows in the mill facing the bakehouse have been stained with the smoke from the chimney. In 2014 Mulberry House contained the still intact Bake House ovens.

William Webb came to Moulton before 1890 and was a miller for A.W. Tindall. His son Herbert from his first marriage was my Grandfather's head baker at Whaplode. His second wife kept a grocery and drapers shop on the corner of the High Road and River Lane together with her daughter and son-in-law, known as Webb and Porter, for many years until the 1950s.

# J T Biggadike

My grandfather was the son of a village inn-keeper and farmer. There was a big drovers inn on what is now the A17 between Fosdyke and Holbeach, known as the 'Saracen's Head', now demolished and leaving the 'New Saracen's Head' a quarter of a mile up the road. Half of the Biggadikes at that time kept pubs and the other half mills. I was the last miller and I don't know of any that still keep public houses.

He didn't have much formal education but came to Moulton School at a penny a week He went to work as everyone did and earned a few pence here and there, later apprenticed to Holmes' baker in Stamford as a boarding baker's boy. He went to London for a while and returned as a baker's assistant to Pode Hole where Mr. Williamson was the baker. In 1888, Grandpa married his wife Elizabeth and they took a small bakery and shop in Peterborough where they stayed for about two years until Whaplode Mill was purchased.

My great grand-parents had six sons and one daughter. The oldest son, William, was born in 1848 and was sixteen years older than my grandfather, who was born in 1864. In 1870 William took the mill at Holbeach Fen. Another son was a master baker in Peterborough.

Whaplode Mill was in what is now Churchgate, on the right-hand side coming in from the High Road. They used to bake bread and deliver as far as Whaplode St. Catherine, finishing alongside the river at about nine-o'clock on Saturday evening. As a youth, Dad held the pony while Grandpa went across the little bridges to serve the customers as the water wasn't as wide as it is now.

The work was hard and people did little else. The highlight of the week was going to chapel or church twice on a Sunday and Sunday School. Villagers could not go further than they could walk, cycle or ride on a horse as there was no public transport. In the villages there was often what was known as a Carriers Cart, which would take parcels and other items to market, including poultry for sale. This cart would also take occasional passengers.

Grandpa went by train to Spalding Corn Market and the cattle market each Tuesday to meet other merchants, to keep up with the prices as well as doing business with farmers by buying their grain and cattle, and taking orders for feed. He would spend the morning in the cattle market and the afternoon in the Corn Exchange. One of the other ways that he was able to keep up-to-date with market prices was to have a copy of the Yorkshire Post delivered to Whaplode Station, which detailed the prices of American wheat. Every morning he would collect the paper and take it home to read. Frank Dring, a local farmer, would call to collect the paper in the afternoon and pay Grandpa half the price.

On Saturday, Grandpa would travel by train to Peterborough Corn Exchange, which stood behind the Parish Church of St. John the Baptist, behind the Butter Cross near the Cathedral, and my father would go with him. I have a list of the stall holders there, including Grandpa who had a stand. Dad decided not to continue with the permanent stand, but bought a walk-in ticket which allowed you to trade when you wanted to attend. The livestock market in Peterborough was behind the Embassy theatre on The Broadway.

Grain which had been threshed was put into sacks with the farmers taking a sample of grain to the various stands, at the corn exchange, where they could compare prices offered by the merchants. The farmer would get his wife to make a sample bag, perhaps out of an old shirt, which would have held two or three pounds. Grandpa would take a look at a farmer's corn and give an opinion as to its price – say 19/- a quarter. The quarter I am talking about is a measure of capacity which starts with four gills and finishes with eight bushels making one quarter. A quarter of wheat weighed four and a half hundred-weight or 36 stone whilst a quarter of barley was thirty two stone and a quarter of oats 24. When it became necessary to deal in tons, the quarter went out of use.

When a farmer offered a sample of grain its quality was assessed by the merchant firstly by smelling the sample to check that it was sweet and not musty. Then a few grains would be bitten to check the dryness and it would be visually checked for its quality. Barley for for malting was also checked by cutting the grain in half using a hand cutter. Dry grain being denser than damp grain. These methods were used throughout my Grandfathers and Fathers time until the introduction of moisture meters, nitrogen testers and the many other electrical and battery operated devices in use today.

Spalding Corn Exchange was a very busy place on Tuesdays (market day). There were stalls with representatives from Corn Merchants, dealers in peas, potatoes, fertilisers, sacks, machinery etc. with farmers coming to buy and sell their produce. The traders who came from a wide area rented their stands and were there every week, while farmers and others paid an entrance fee of 2d. Some farmers preferred to stand alongside the White Hart Hotel nearby and conduct their business there in the hope that, if successful, they would be treated to a whisky or other refreshment by the purchasers. In earlier times, alongside the Corn Exchange, was what was known as the Buttermarket, where farmers' wives would sell their butter, cheese, eggs and dressed poultry etc.

When Grandpa bought from farmers he would sell on to a middle merchant who would, in turn, trade it through the bigger corn exchanges such as Lincoln, Leeds, Liverpool or Mark Lane in London. The ownership of the grain could change several times before it was loaded onto the railways. It was then moved by rail from Moulton, Spalding or Holbeach Goods yard. Over the years middle merchants became redundant; flour millers now purchase their wheat on a strict specification from large grain stores.

Anyway, the story of the farmer. Our stand was just inside the door. He came in with his sample of corn and Grandpa would say how much he would give for the wheat. Grandpa would tell him a certain price, maybe nineteen shillings. The farmer would say that he wasn't going to take that. Then Grandpa would ask whether he would take a pound. The farmer wasn't keen and went to see what the rest of the dealers would pay.

If Grandpa had stuck to the exact price then the other merchants would have bought it. As Grandpa was beside the door, the farmer returned and said that he would take the pound for the corn as Grandpa had offered. Grandpa said he had asked whether the farmer would take a pound. He didn't say that he would give him a pound. He was able to buy the corn, but he wasn't able to try this trick very often as the farmers soon became aware of his ploy.

As Grandpa prospered he bought pieces of land, in total about 70 acres, and rented 30 more. His family kept increasing year by year and in due course, when my father was about 14, Grandfather left the Whaplode Mill house having bought a nearby farm called 'the Sycamores'. He left the older family behind and took with him the children who were still at school. He bought anything that he thought would sell and in about 1903/4 purchased three cottages for £45. The old ladies living in them paid half-a-crown a week rent, and although he thought that this was a good return on his money, he was so pleased when he sold them, vacant, and made £650 for them in about 1950.

There were no representatives going round, and no telephones. Grandpa was into direct buying and selling. As time wore on, Grandpa got a good reputation and even when delivering bread he was able to help farmers with merchanting while he took a margin of profit.

As a youth of 16, Dad would have driven cattle to market and one day he had taken animals from Whaplode into Spalding. After the sale Dad had asked Grandpa whether all the animals had been sold. Grandpa replied that they had and so Dad was happy as he thought he could go home by train. Much to his surprise his Dad told him that they had been sold to a farmer from Whaplode Fen and he was to take them there. In total Dad walked fifteen miles that day, from Whaplode to Spalding, back to Whaplode Fen and finally returning home to

Whaplode.

My grandparents had 12 children, the eldest son being Arthur who was two years older than my father. My father was always known to everyone as Jack. Following them were three sisters and the next boys were much younger than Dad or Uncle Arthur.

Leading up to the time when Grandfather sold out, the business continued in much the same way. The Great War was near and Dad and Arthur were of military age, they were called up in 1916 with only 6 weeks between them being at home and being in the trenches, that was all the training you got. At some time in the war Arthur was gassed and it always left him asthmatic. Dad was shot in the leg after he went over the top, sustaining a flesh wound through the calf, with the bullet going straight through without touching the bone. It probably saved his life and got him out of the line and home for convalescence. After his return to France he became a Morse code and flags signaller.

Grandpa's daughter, Doris had continued his bread round and I think he found it difficult to keep the show going without a son at home. Late on a Saturday evening a family called who said they were sorry to call so late but they had no bread. Doris would not leave any as they owed money. Grandpa told her off, saying she should never leave children without bread. Grandpa was a kindly thoughtful man whose motto was that he should make enough money to provide for himself and his family and then to step back and let others do the same.

I have the bill of sale for when he sold the Whaplode Mill in

1917 to Sinclairs from Boston, who had two or three mills in the district. They moved a manager into the mill house.

What was Grandpa's thinking in selling the Whaplode Mill when he had two older sons who would soon return from the Great War? I realised over the years that Grandpa had foreseen that trade would not be so good after the war as there might be an agricultural slump. He realised that he had about £5000 due to him in the ledgers and that this was a lot of money. One could retire on £2000 capital and a new house would cost below £500. By the time it had been collected, he would be a relatively rich man He was shrewd and this was proved with the benefit of hindsight. When Father and Uncle Arthur returned from the Great War they were left at the farm as partners. With them was Bill aged 17 or 18, with one of their sisters to keep house for them.

In the early days the flour produced by such mills as Whaplode and Moulton would have been the only flour available. As time went on flour became entirely different. The flour you would have got from ordinary grinding would have been wholemeal, not white which was what the people wanted. The Derbyshire Peak stones were used to produce animal feed, unlike the French Burr stones which would have been used for flour, until the roller mills came in.

Grandpa and many bakers in the area used to buy flour from Mr. Tindall at Holbeach. This mill processed wheat into white flour using the proper machinery with a proportion of English wheat blended with harder Canadian wheat. With modern breeding of new varieties, harder varieties of wheat are now able to be grown in this country.

Tindall supplied Grandpa with flour in 10 stone sacks for use in the bakehouse, and some were re-packaged for retail customers into bags containing a stone in weight. Farmer's wives would buy a stone, or in the case of people who had large families, a 5 or 10 stone sack at a time would be purchased.

One day he called into a farmhouse with the bread and said that the farmer's wife hadn't bought any flour for the house lately. She said that she had been buying it direct from Tindall as it was cheaper than his. Grandpa replied that he was sorry, but he could not reduce his price. When he next saw Tindall at Spalding Market he told him that he had been supplying flour to one of his customers, cheaper than he supplied him at the bakehouse. Tindall replied that it was a free country and so it was all right to charge what he liked. They didn't fall out but several weeks later Mr. Tindall remarked to Grandpa that he hadn't been buying any flour for the bakehouse. In reply Grandpa told Tindall that it was a free country and he would be getting it elsewhere. I do not know where he got it from locally so it must have come by train. This reflects the way business worked at that time.

Grandfather retired to Spalding with the 6 youngest children ranging from 8 to 19 years of age. Grandfather kept on merchanting corn and cattle dealing, and as a result was kept fully occupied after withdrawing from the milling and baking business.

# Threshing

When a farmer intended to thresh, one of the first things he would do was to hire the railway sacks. While he was at the station he would order the coal for the threshing machine as the thresher men did not supply the coal. In the 1900s during Grandpa's hey-day, an enterprising threshing machine owner, Joe Cade, from Whaplode, had ten threshing sets and a nucleus of full time men with up to one hundred seasonal workers. The sheaves of corn were kept in stacks, or in some cases at harvesting time threshed straight out of the field. Certainly in my early days the threshing machine would have been working for most of the year. They always said that in Joe Cade's time his men threshed ten months of the year and his regular men would then spend the next two months maintaining the machinery for the following season.

There were eleven men in a threshing unit. The engine driver, who had a boy for carrying water to the engine. A man who stood on the drum to spread and feed the corn into the drum. Behind him would have been a man cutting the bands off the sheaves, which had been passed forward by one of two men on the stack. Another man stood behind the drum dealing with the straw, straightening it out, tying it into large bundles which were then hooked onto an endless wire to the top of another stack. Two men on top would stack the straw and raise the pole so that the continuous wire was always on top of the stack. In later times the straw would have been baled. There was someone doing the dirtiest job you could find, which was by the pulp hole where all the chaff left the machine. This was dropped onto sheets and had to be carried away, some of it was kept as animal feed while the rest dumped and burnt.

The corn carrier was paid a penny or tuppence an hour more than the rest, taking the 18-stone sacks, on his back, the short distance to where it was to be stored. If the corn was running very quickly there might be two men carrying the corn. This was really hard work.

Not only had Joe Cade got all these threshing machines he also owned and lived at the 'Lamb and Flag' pub in Whaplode. A lot of these men were itinerant workers and it is said that he got these workers, those living in the barns, - the seasonal workers -, to spend their money on the slate at his pub and on a Friday night, at he end of the week, they would not draw much wages as a result.

There were four pubs in the village. The 'Bell and Bowl' was near the church, the 'Ram' in Churchgate, the 'Star' and the 'Lamb and Flag' on the High Road. When it was turning-out time on a Friday or Saturday night, when the men had been paid, Dad and his brother had to go out to the yard to stop the workers from dossing down in their yard. The Lamb and Flag is now the only pub open in the village.

Joe Cade bought farms and at one time owned the 'White Hart' in Spalding. When Lloyd George brought in the law that employers had to pay a national insurance stamp for each of their employees, Joe Cade wouldn't pay. Eventually the bailiffs were brought in and possessed goods to the value of the debt, which they took to Spalding auction. He still wouldn't pay so Mrs. Cade went down to the auction and bought them all back. They were a very independent sort of people.

Joe Cade had built his businesses and it went on for three more generations with the last generation the same age as me. He tried to keep it going during the time when combine harvesters were coming in. Combine harvesters would be in use for a few weeks of the year and could complete the total job of harvesting in a far shorter time, with a saving in man power. This new style of farming encouraged the farmers to buy their own combine harvester resulting in the end of threshing. Just like the village mill, threshing was overtaken by technology.

# Moulton Railway Station

Moulton Station was on the Midland and Great Northern Line ("muddle and go nowhere", M.G.N. had this undeserved nickname) later becoming part of the L.N.E.R. There was one line which went straight through with five sidings and shed, unlike Whaplode and Weston which could only receive parcels. The station was used by most farmers to carry their produce of corn, potatoes, sugar beet and many others. If we went away for a few days to Yarmouth then we got on the train at Moulton and travelled all the way to the sea. If we fancied a day at the seaside we could catch a Sunday day excursion to 'Sunny Hunny' which was (and still is) the colloquial name for Hunstanton.

The station was a very busy place. There was a coal merchant's office employing three workmen and a manager, two men with a lorry delivering and one in the yard to serve customers. All households needed coal for heating and cooking. There was a parcel office, as many items were delivered by rail, and you could even send a basket of racing pigeons to be released at a distant station and the empty basket would get returned.

The line was dualled at the station with a platform either side; this was the only passing point between Spalding and Holbeach. The system that was employed on most single-track lines was called the satchel or token system. Mostly at stations, a token in its satchel, with a very large handle, could be exchanged between the engine's fireman and the signalman, enabling the receiving train to proceed to the next section. The Tablet or Token was hung from a gantry which enabled it to be picked up without stopping. The last two signalmen were Fred Leverington and Fred Whenn, who lived close to the station and took it in turns to be on duty. There were several pieces of land beside the line which were used as allotments by railway staff. Three porters were employed at Moulton Station and at least two of them lived in the gatehouses where their wives opened the crossing gates. There were a number of station masters in my memory and they lived in the Station House. I remember Mr. Thomas, Mr. Postle and lastly Mr. Holliday. In my parents time there was a station master at Weston and one at Whaplode, but latterly a clerk was the only staff employed with Moulton's station master travelling between the three stations.

The senior clerk, Mr. Self. lived in the village, and two men worked in the office dealing with any paperwork, but these jobs were taken over by ladies when the men were called into the navy. On most days Dad travelled down to the station on his bike to see if any orders had come through and to order trucks with their sheets. A railway truck usually carried 9 tons which was 80 sacks, or four trips for our lorry

All the grain was put into railway sacks, hired from the railway; the hire charge being a penny a week. If it was returned full to the railway, as the railway were transporting the full sack then the cost was reduced to half a penny. The farmers went to the local station to collect their sacks and they were filled at the farm. They were then transferred between the farmer and the merchant as the buyer, finally the merchant to the miller who returned the empty sack to the railway. The railways were particular about their sacks and if sacks were missing then they were charged about 5/-, but the merchant could probably supply a missing sack if necessary. Corn merchants would often carry a small float of sacks which they acquired from errors in counting.

When the railways ceased their sack hire system Chisholm, Fox and Garner had a similar 'rent-a-sack' scheme, and Tindall ran the local depot.

Nine sacks of grain could be carried on a cart. The horse man would walk beside the horse and ride back on the empty cart. In those times, that number of sacks would have been dealt with easily. When the mill obtained its first lorry, it carried 20 sacks, approximately two tons. You couldn't load one of the big modern lorries on your own now as it would be beyond anyone's capacity. Now almost all grain transported in bulk.

# The Bake House and Mill House

Probably before A.W.Tindall first rented the mill, the bakehouse was let to Fred Webster, who I believe was a relative of Mrs A.C.King and he also had the grocer's shop which is now the village Post Office. This, I believe was also owned by the Kings at that time. At almost all mills there was a bakehouse as at Whaplode Mill in my Grandfathers time. No doubt, the King family operated the Moulton bakehouse for bread using their own flour until the bakehouse was separated from the Mill.

In 1906 John William Widdows, a young baker from Murrow, near Wisbech, who I remember well, took over the bakehouse. I remember the delicious smell and taste of the newly baked bread. He married a local lady born in Weston who was also a partner with her sister in the grocer's and general store opposite. They had one son, John William Widdows Junior, who was born in 1912. Unfortunately Mrs Widdows died in 1922 and Mr. Widdows lived with a house keeper, Miss Roe, a little further along High Street. J.W.W. Jnr, always known as Jack, grew up and joined his father in the business, taking over in 1937. There was always another employee - a baker's roundsman - and perhaps an apprentice as well. Bread and cakes were delivered daily around the district by Jack and by Charlie Craske, a long-term employee. Undoubtedly deliveries were made by horse-drawn bakers van in earlier days.

Upon Jack's marriage in 1945, he left the village to take a bakery business in Nottingham and the bakery was taken by George Adcock, a local man, born in the village who continued until the business closed down in the mid-1950s John William Widdows Senior continued to work in the bakehouse until this point.

The Mill House was situated to the right-hand side of the 14ft. road leading to the mill, with the bakehouse on the left hand side. The Mill House was entered directly from the roadway to the Mill. Although this was safe in earlier times, as traffic increased to the mill it became a dangerous entrance. The House was demolished 1960. Pettit's undertook the demolition, taking the material to be used as hardcore. Adjoining the Mill House was a garage for Claude King, a coal house and flour store. When the Mill House was demolished a piece of a beam from the building, dated 1791, was kept and later given to Mr. and Mrs. Teeuw the present owners of Mulberry House.

My father married Ida Dean in 1925. Ida was a farmer's daughter from Weston. They lived in the Mill House for two years before they bought a house in Broad Lane which Mum named 'Hazeldene' after the trees in the garden and her birth surname. Dad took over the lease of the Mill Shop, which was, as it had been for a long time, a cobbler's shop for an additional £5 on his half-yearly rent. My parents' bedroom was over the shop and they appreciated the quiet at night as he could control the shop's opening hours. I was born in 1929 in Hazeldene and lived there all of my life until 2001.

William Mears was a miller with my Grandfather at Whaplode and I believe he had been at Moulton Mill as a young man. When Grandpa sold the mill, William continued to work for him and later for my father and uncle on the farm (1917-1924).

When my father took Moulton Mill, William came as a miller and after Father bought Hazeldene House, came to live in the Mill House. After the death of his wife in 1932 he left the house, but continued to work at the mill for several more years.

Fred Ford was employed by the King family from about 1921, living with his family in the Mill House. He was horseman and worked on Kings farm as well as at the Mill. They left the Mill House in 1925 and my parents lived there for 2½ years. Fred moved into a cottage and shortly afterwards moved again into a new Council House in East Cobgate, living there for the rest of his life. Fred was employed by my father as delivery man, firstly by horse and trolley, and when the first lorry was bought in 1932, Fred learned to drive and continued to enjoy work as a lorry man, and later in the Mill until his death in 1968 at the age of 78. Thus Fred completed a total of 47 years' service at the Mill.

After serving in the Great War, Frank Davison came to Moulton from North Lincolnshire in the 1920s as a baker working in Rowers Bakery. When Mears left the Mill House, he came to us as a miller and at that time we had three full-time employees. He remained with us for 25 years until his death in 1958. Frank continued to keep his hand in at baking on Friday nights as a night baker at Rowers. After his death, the Mill House was no longer occupied and it was demolished in the early 1960s.

These three employees and faithful friends were at the Mill, two from before I was born and one from me being three years old. In the case of Fred Ford he continued working for me after my father's death. I worked alongside Fred and Frank all my youth, benefiting greatly from their experience.

After Fred decided to give up the lorry work and later after Frank's death, we had a number of employees, all from local families, who were with us for shorter periods. They left and moved on for various reasons, but all became lifelong friends of mine as was usually the case in a family business. This is a way of life which is fast disappearing.

# Mr. J. T. Biggadike Junior

In 1921 Arthur Cowley King was still alive and after Tindall's departure, Arthur's son Claude who was not a very robust man decided to do a bit of milling in partnership with his younger brother Leslie. I think they had to bring in a portable engine to drive the mill, in order to grind the local farmer's corn. The family had independent means and farmed land in the village so there was no need to earn a living from the Mill. Their bill heads show 'C.A.M. and A.L. King', millers. Arthur Cowley King died in 1923 and the mill was let to my father in 1924 which must have been to Claude King's relief.

The period after the Great War was a period of depression in the farming industry. Dad lived at the farm in Whaplode until 1924, when he heard that Moulton Mill was available to rent. The Kings, after three years' milling, had decided to let the mill, rather than run it themselves. At that time there was not much milling business attached to the mill as the King brothers had mainly ground farmer's corn. Claude had promised that the redundant flour machinery would be removed but he never kept this promise and it remained there until after his death. There was little useful space in the two rooms and only a narrow passage way alongside the machinery with the only usable part of the upper floor being the rear third.

Dad preferred to be a miller and having decided to rent the mill, withdrew from the farming partnership with his brother, and although they had far more stock in the farm inventory, it was worth about the same as when they had taken over from Grandfather.

Grandpa had kept on the corn trading side of his business and, after Dad took over the mill, he also took over the grain trading business from his father. He combined this with the cattle cake purchasing business which created a secure enterprise. Once the trading business had transferred to Dad, he traded as J.T. Biggadike Jnr, as you can see by the stand from Spalding Corn Exchange. The stand belonged to the Corn Exchange but on its closure we were allowed to retain it. At night the wooden stands would have been folded and stored away when the room was used for dances or meetings. Grandpa would have been about sixty and he had retired, having said that when tax went up to 6d in the pound it was time to retire, but he drew a small remuneration for helping Dad at the markets.

Dad's reputation in the business quickly became known. One of the first customers of Dad's business, on the first or second page of the initial register, was named Oldershaw and his grandson was my last customer. His Grandson contrived to collect his last order by horse and trolley in the same way as his Grandfather had done many years before.

When Dad had taken the mill in 1924 there was no engine power there. He had to have power to drive the mill so he and Grandpa went to the County Show, which at that time travelled around from site to site. They saw a Lincoln manufactured Ruston and Hornsby, a 25hp, single cylinder diesel engine with a five feet diameter fly wheel. This stood about six feet in length with a cylinder that was about 12 inches in diameter. Dad bought one, through the agency of Peacock and Binnington of Brigg. Records from the manufacturer's archives record that the machine was a 6H oil engine rated at 25hp/

300rpm, number 122377 sold to my father on 4<sup>th</sup> September 1924.

It was delivered and installed by the makers onto a concrete bed of their specifications, about eighteen inches high. Their engineers would have stayed in the village for a few days, whilst they built and commissioned the engine. If the engine needed attention then they always sent an engineer by train from Lincoln, arriving at Moulton Station. If the job was to take longer than a day then he would stay overnight. It was so well installed there was no vibration and you could stand a penny edgeways on the engine. Nowadays an engineer would just drive over from Lincoln and return the same day.

The engine stood in the engine shed where the present kitchen now stands. The mill was driven from the drive wheel by fast and loose pulleys. The big belt drove a five-feet wheel which in turn drove the shafts that are still in situ under the ground floor in the Mill. One set of gears drives the stones on the first floor, while another belt drove a parallel shaft with a set of gears which drove the vertical shaft. The vertical drive meant we could operate the sack hoist, but only when using the bottom set of stones. We had to go down into the basement, through the trap door outside the miller's office, to oil the gearing every day. This was one of the miller's jobs but sometimes I did it.

Had we needed it, the engine could have been run for 24 hours a day as two, 400 gallon water drums had been installed outside the engine house to act as cooling tanks. Most of the time we carried the buckets of water up from the cistern to top up the tank. One winter the tank had to be replaced with a single 300 gallon tank, standing ten feet high, that was

# Photographs

*The Mill before the sails were wrecked in December 1894*

*Robert King,
the Mill
Builder*

*Robert King's
son, James
Measure King*

*Claude King (seated), William Mears and*
*Fred Pettit (standing) from a photo of*
*Moulton Bowls Club taken in 1930.*

*The Mill at Whaplode that was operated by my Grandfather who is
shown standing by the window with my father, aged 2, in the dress*

*Grandfather with one of his two best horses,
Dick who was conscripted into WW1*

*A Picture from 1938 the Three millers - from l to r G W Plowman, A W Tindall, J Biggadike Snr who all celebrated their Golden Weddings that year. Photo courtesy of Lincolnshire Free Press.*

*A view of Moulton High Street showing the Bake House and the Bakers cart*

*Grandfather*

*My Father who took over
Moulton Mill in 1924*

*The Last miller of
Moulton Mill*

*The Mill and Moulton Church before 1928 when the cap was replaced*

*A photo from 1928 showing the new cap with Zak Baxter, a local tradesman (on the top), on the balcony are Les King and Horace Ford and at the bottom, my Father and Fred Ford*

*Fred Ford with our first lorry*

*Joe Evans, the Millwright and Frank Davison
working on the stones*

*Frank Davison and Fred Ford at the front door of the Mill*

*Three generations of the Widdows family who were bakers in Moulton from 1906 until 1945*

*Spalding Corn exchange in 1953*

*Spalding Corn exchange in 1954*
*Both photos courtesy of Lincolnshire Free Press.*

*Moulton Railway Station*

*Moulton Railway Station*
*showing the goods yard and sidings on the left*

*A view of Moulton
High Street showing
the Mill House*

*Below A view from the other
direction showing Mulberry House,
the King Family residence the Bake
House as the last building on the
right of the picture.*

*Fount Hemmant and me during the replacement
of the cap covering in 1971*

*Clifford Clark during
the same project*

*View of the Mill from the East showing the grain storage bins*

*Farm vehicles queuing down the road to the Mill in 1976*

*Watching the grain being poured into a pit*

*Maureen and me*

Me in my prime (Well, almost)

sufficient for our needs as we only ran the engine for four or five hours a day. I remember, as a boy, watching the men carry the water up in buckets to top up this three hundred gallon drum with 200 or 300 buckets of water. They said that the icicles reached from one stave (step) to another. When the engine had been running for several hours and you climbed the ladder, with a couple of buckets of water, to the top of the tank you could feel the lovely warm water in which you could have had a bath, though to my knowledge, no-one ever did. Eventually a pump was fitted to raise the water and fill the tank.

The engine was started using a compressed air cylinder, standing at least four feet in height and 18 inches in diameter, operating at a pressure of 200 lb. per square inch. As regulations came in we had to have it officially pressure tested annually. When the valves on the compressed air bottle were opened then the escaping air turned the engine and you waited until the engine had enough revs. A valve was operated which cut off the air supply from the cylinder, then you had to be fairly quick to operate the control for the diesel to take over. There was a small drive shaft off the engine which enabled you to recharge the bottle with air ready for the next time. Occasionally, especially in cold weather, the engine wouldn't start and you had lost all in air in the bottle in which case you had to use the starting handle. The handle was two and a half feet in length and needed two men to turn it. The handle was extended to three feet to permit two men to stand side by side. If more help was needed a rope could be attached to increase the force available. Fred Pettit, the blacksmith, was a friend of ours so he was always contacted and we would lend us some of his men to pull on the rope until we had got the engine started. If we went across the road at a certain time of the day then he would always know what we wanted.

When the engine was running nicely you went into the mill, right in the corner, where the flour is now displayed. There was a lever that you pulled to move the belt over from the loose pulley to the fast one. For the first half a minute everyone in the vicinity, especially to the rear of the mill where the sound carried, knew that we were starting up the machinery. You could hear the engine cough rather loudly, until the stones gained the momentum from the dead start, then peace returned. All the visitors to the mill, especially the small boys, wanted to see the engine working.

In the late fifties after our miller died, we sold the engine, as there was a demand for them, (with several firms buying engines for the export business). It was said at the time that most went to Iraq for pumping water. I think we received almost as much as it had cost. In many ways it would have been nice to still have the engine but the present kitchen could not have been there.

When the engine had gone and the ground was flat we bricked up the inside of the wooden shed but left the outside boarding to improve its appearance to our neighbours and it was used to store twenty or thirty tons of grain inside the engine shed. We had to clamber on top to level it and the dust made this very difficult in such a low shed.

At that time the main supplementary feed for the cattle was linseed or cotton cake. The firms supplying these products had reps at the local markets. They also had stands at the big shows, such as Peterborough and Lincolnshire, where orders could be placed and forward contracts negotiated. There is an advertising board for one of these companies in the mill. There were adverts in the local papers showing that cotton seed cake would have come from Egyptian cotton seed. These products were among the main feeds supplied to farmers, in Dad's earliest days at the mill, together with ground oats and bran for horses, barley meal and middlings for pigs and maize and wheat for poultry. Bran and middlings are by-products of flour milling and were purchased from flour mills. Linseed and cotton cake was purchased from a firm in Hull and during the winter months we regularly received 5 ton loads delivered to Moulton Station.

Every farmer had a cake breaker, for the large slabs of feed, which were about 30in wide, 12in deep, and weighed a stone each, which needed care as you turned the large handle so as not to injure your fingers. Care had to be taken with cotton cake as we normally carried four slabs at a time and, being softer than linseed cake, it could break when being handled and you could have dropped the rest of the load on your feet. Mears had a special apron, which hung on a door, for carrying cotton cake because if you didn't wear one, a yellow-green deposit was left on your clothes.

Just outside the office there used to be enough room to make a high stack of cake. William Mears was there answering the phone in the office when the cake stack slipped, trapping him inside the office. The stones were running and being in the mill on his own there was going to be a problem. The lorry driver, Fred Ford, came in at the vital moment, looked at Mears who was agitated and frantically waving his arms around, checked on the stones to see that a meal sack spout was not clogged and finally released him.

The Mill's horses were kept in the stable at the back of the Mill but as Tindall continued to rent the grass field, where Gardman's is now, Dad used to have to take the horses to Uncle Arthur's paddock at Cobgate, in Whaplode, for the weekends. Mother used to keep chickens in the Mill Yard but to Arthur Tindall's consternation they used to wander on to his grass field and eat the grass. Eventually Mr Tindall's concerns led to Dad erecting chicken wire fencing along the boundary.

Sometimes we kept the horse, named Joe, in the small paddock at Hazeldene House, but during the summer months and often at the end of a day's work it would be walked to Uncle Arthur's field at Cobgate in Whaplode. Even after we had obtained a lorry we kept the horse and that is where I came on the scene. Joe wasn't a large animal and when I and my friends were about seven or eight we used to capture this long suffering creature and clamber onto his back. Holding him gently he would travel until he got fed up and then he would pass under low-growing trees, sweeping us off. Occasionally one of the local farmers would borrow him if they needed an extra horse. When I was about nine and still at primary school Joe died.

After I had left school and was helping Dad, I also kept poultry and hatched eggs then sold the day old chicks and ducklings. I expanded it at Hazeldene House until at my peak I had a thousand hens in deep litter houses, whereas Mum always had them in little arks. I have a photograph of myself at about two years of age surrounded by chickens, so I was thoroughly familiar with poultry.

Along the lane where the post mill had been situated on the High Road, there was land which was administered by the Parish Council. This nine-acre field had grazing rights for nine animals between May and October. The Parish liked to have six cows and three horses, as cows were better at grazing the grass hummocks. Dad had the grazing rights for one cow on the field. Now the field is let as a single entity. As a youth, in the Summer, I used to travel down Bell Lane with the cow on the way to her pasture on the parish grazing field, off the High Road. For all of my working life, I got pleasure from keeping and milking a cow.

In 1931/2 the government had introduced the Wheat Commission Scheme and in this a payment was made to the farmer, over and above what he made on the market. All the merchants had to be registered with the scheme in order to administer it. Books of wheat certificates were issued which Dad had to complete, in order to certify how much had been paid to the farmer. This information in the form of the wheat certificates had to be counter-signed by the farmer before being sent to the Wheat Commission. This continued until the Second World War when the government brought in fixed prices. Dad used to say that in the thirties business was just beginning to get into order when another war broke out.

After the Second World War had finished the Fixed Price system ceased and the government introduced the Cereal

Deficiency Payment Scheme. This was similar to the Wheat Commission Scheme and it successfully continued until we entered the Common Market in 1973 and the Common Agricultural Policy subsidy system replaced our national one.

In 1932 Dad bought our first lorry, holding twenty sacks, which was about 2¼ ton. Previously all of our deliveries were done by horse and trolley. Fred Ford was our driver and he learned to drive this new lorry.

In my father's time in business, the longest of the three of us, agricultural life continued with few changes. One significant change was that the use of horses began to decline, with the development of affordable tractors. On most small farms this was in the form of the 'Fergie' Ferguson tractor. This small grey vehicle with its hard iron bucket seat, and no protection from the weather, was the first tractor that many farmers possessed. Most farmers would attempt to mitigate the worst of the discomfort by putting a sack on the seat.

Threshing still continued from the stack although combine harvesters were introduced during the war. This farm mechanisation meant a big change for the village miller, although up until the time of Dad's death in 1964 we never handled bulk grain but increasingly it was handled in that way. Some provender millers and merchants began to expand their businesses more than Dad did, as a response to the bigger farmers' increased use of combine harvesters.

The first combine harvesters delivered harvested and threshed grain into sacks on the machine. In my early years there was no moisture tester, it was done all by the feel of the sack, the skill and experience of the farmer and the miller. Dry corn is denser than wet. If the corn was damp then you could hardly get the sack tied up if it contained the correct weight but if it was dry then you had plenty of neck to tie.

As these early machines put their threshed grain into sacks with the straw ejected from the machine straight onto the ground, we were still able to continue as before. Later a baling machine followed, but if the straw was not required then it was fired or burned. Near-by housewives had to watch out for the falling ash from the burning straw, as did motorists on adjacent roads, when the burning smoke might be blown straight across the road.

Electricity was installed in 1952. From 1958 the new hoist and the plate mill were fitted with electric motors which made their operation much simpler. After the engine's disposal the stones were not used at all, having been superseded by the hammer mill. The plate mill, used for splitting maize, which was then sieved for poultry feed, was not used during the war years as little or no maize was imported.

Installed in 1958, the hammer mill was situated in the warehouse on the left as one entered from the mill. Opposite this was a mixer which was used to mix meal and protein mix to produce our own pig and poultry feeds. All pellets and cubes were bought in, as we did not have the machinery to produce them, nor the quantity of business to justify buying it. We used this equipment from 1958 until the time I retired in 1995.

As time went on, the composition of animal feedstuffs developed as animal nutrition became more scientific. The motive behind this scientific approach was the requirements of more rapid and therefore more profitable growth.

Compound feeds were produced initially by national feed companies and later by all in the industry. Compound feeds had added protein in the form of fishmeal, (a by-product of the fishing industry), meat and bone meal, and minerals. Protein and mineral mixtures were then produced enabling small millers and farmers to add to their cereals.

Using these supplements, we produced two types of pig feed, one for breeding sows and weaners, and the other for fattening. We also produced two types of poultry mash, one for layers and the other for growers. Baby chick mash and crumbs, baby pig pellets, cattle cubes, including ones for milk production and all other pellets and cubes were bought in.

All compound feed analysis had to be declared on the bag labels, oil, protein and fibre were listed and samples were regularly taken by Weights and Measures Inspectors for analysis.

## Fred Pettit

Fred Pettit kept the Swan Inn and was also the local blacksmith. He employed a couple of men and shod the shire horses in the blacksmith's shop adjoining the Swan pub. He was a very enterprising businessman who began to convert the farm Scotch carts, changing their shafts for a tow bar, so they could be towed by a tractor. He then set out to build a purpose built complete cart, carrying about three tons, with hydraulic tipping gear. He continued the tradition of having the farmer's name on the front of the cart for some time.

He quickly used the piece of land behind the Swan which had been a kitchen garden. There was a row of buildings including the club room and these were filled with all of his spares. The garden was soon covered with a strong corrugated iron shed. At that time planning permission was not required, it was just intrinsic growth of his business. He put in electric powered hammers, the vibrations from which, when they were all working together, could be felt in Hazeldene House.

The business kept on expanding and he bought the field next to the mill, where Gardman's factory is now. He erected the building, one bay at a time, employing a full-time bricklayer to keep up with the increase in his business. Many of the village school leavers went to work at Pettit's and learned their trades from his senior employees.

He attended all the big agricultural shows, the Smithfield Show in London, the Royal Show as well as several county shows. At one time he employed much of the local labour, as many as 40 people, exporting these trailers to twenty-seven countries. Everyone in farming knows what a Pettit trailer is and his company also made lots of other farm equipment.

Fred Pettit had only one daughter, who was handicapped, so eventually when he had to dispose of the business he sold it to part of the Geest organisation. Fred Pettit's works manager and his office manager left to set up their own manufacturing business. Geests were under agreement with Fred Pettit to continue the same type of business for ten years. After ten years Geests closed the business and sold the site to one of the two sons of Van Geest. He used the offices as his headquarters and the building as a potato store as this was a major part of his business, later selling out to Gardmans.

## Milling Operations

This section is here because it is common to both my father and me, and in fact much of it holds for the whole history of the Mill.

We would fill the ground floor with sacks and then we would have a session of lifting. Until we got electricity you couldn't run the hoist independently of the stones - you had to grind, using the bottom stones, at the same time as you were lifting.

Once we got electricity it became possible to run the hoist on its own. You learnt with practice how to operate the hoist, and if you eased on the rope then the chain would slowly lower the sack under its own weight. You would, ease the rope when the sack had come through the door and weight of the sack would lower it onto the floor.

When you were filling bins on the sixth floor from the dust floor then a weight, about 2 stones (28lb or 13kg) similar to the ones on the meal floor, would be tied onto the sack hoist control rope.  On the dust floor there was an empty wooden nine gallon beer barrel with this weight resting on it and still tied to the hoist rope. When you wanted the hoist to work you took the weight from off the barrel and let it hang to operate the hoist, lifting the next sack up the mill. This method allowed sufficient time to empty the previous sack into the bin, before the new full sack arrived.

If you were filling a bin, using the sack hoist, then there were two tail chains for attaching the sacks with the bottom half of each chain highly polished, due to the amount of use it had received.

Two tie chains were only useful if you were on the top floor. You could only have one sack on the hoist at a time. When you had taken the sack off the chain, the chain would remain where it was. The quickest method to get the next sack up was for the person loading sacks on to the hoist at the bottom to pull the chain round, so that the second tie chain appeared, or to pull the tie chain back down to the ground floor.

As the grain came in from the farmers, we knew where each sack had come from and the full sacks were stacked around the bottom floor. We would have a session pulling the lot onto the reefing floor, while we would have been grinding at the same time.

Frank Davison always wore a warehouse coat. One day, as well as putting the chain around the sack, he got part of his coat in the loop of chain that was holding the sack. I was pulling on the third floor, but didn't look down. Suddenly Frank's head appeared through the trap door. I was told "keep pulling and don't let go." I pulled him up, then gently let him down and he vanished down the stairs quicker than he had come up. He had enough presence of mind to sit on the sack. Obviously he thought that the shock of seeing him would have made me let go of the rope.

The old story of the boy hitching a lift on the sack is a bit stretched. Heber (Nicky) Nicholls always used to say that he went up on the chain but the millers would never have allowed that and there would have had to be someone operating the rope. I remember on occasions, as a boy, going up to the next floor and opening the trap doors and gripping the chain. The weight of the chain would act as a counter-balance, enabling me to be lowered gently down to the floor below.

I also remember Dad grinding maize for horses using the top stones, but as he was worried about damaging the spur wheel, he bought a plate mill which stood between the small stones and the door in the warehouse.

When we wanted to stack corn sacks in the tower, we would lower the sack onto a table, making it easier to lift it onto your back. If a new man was operating the hoist then he might yank it up and down between the floor and ceiling because he wasn't using the hoist gently. When electricity had been installed then the hoist was still controlled by a rope but driven by an electric motor, which had a brake. You had the same control as when it was a friction hoist. We even used to stack sacks of barley on the stone floor on top of the stones, which is why the stone crane and other equipment was removed.

Each farmer's small quantity of grain was milled separately, so the farmers' sacks were piled on the reefing floor so that we could identify them. The small trap door on the reefing floor, next to the staircase was used to fill the small bin below. This in turn fed the stones on the first floor. A door on the floor below (the 2nd floor), which opened inwards was kept shut by the weight of the grain inside the bin. When full, this bin contained one ton of grain which allowed for about two hours of grinding.

The corn came down the short wooden chute, onto which was attached a sacking sleeve. The chute led to the wooden hopper above the bottom stones. This hopper would hold enough for ten minutes grinding. When all the farmer's grain was in the wooden hopper, you would tie the sacking sleeve in order to stop the next farmer's grain from escaping into the hopper, so mixing two farmer's grain together. You would need to run up two flights of steps as quickly as possible so you could empty the next farmer's grain into the bin. You would come down bringing the empty sacks with you, throw them to your man by the meal chute on the bottom floor to be refilled with meal (animal feed). You would never let the stone run out of corn. If you only had a couple of sacks for each farmer then you would be tearing up and down the steps every ten minutes. This was part of our daily routine and at times it became pretty hectic.

A farmer who needed feed weekly would bring a full load of grain into the mill which would fill one of the bins, to be kept solely for him. In my time we worked mainly on the floor where the gallery is. We had converted the bins on the upper floors to feed the bottom stones.

There is a shutter with a handle above the hole into the bin now used as the archive room. Before we had a mixing machine we used this bin to mix the meal with a light-weight aluminium meal shovel. This was poured into the bin from the reefing floor above and, when the dust had settled, we used to go in to mix the meal, leaving the door open. The animal feed would then be sent to the bottom floor, through the wide chute by the tea room door, where it would be sacked off.

When a new stone weighing about a ton, arrived 'wet', as it had been freshly cut out of the hillside, it would be left in the mill to season. The only one I remember must have arrived in the late thirties and we stored it for several years under the stairs until it was needed. If you look above the outside of the front door the bricks have grooves in them. To get the stone off the lorry they put blocks and pulleys out of the window and attached the bottom pulley to the stone. The cuts in the bricks have been caused by the chains rubbing on the brickwork as the stone was manoeuvred inside. A new stone is not as dangerous to move as a worn one, due to its greater depth of twelve inches. When the bed stone became too thin to use it would be removed, the current running stone would take its place, as the bed stone, and the new stone installed as the running stone.

When it was taken from its storage place it had to be lifted to the floor where it was to be used. If you look carefully at the trap door, you will see on the floor, next to it, an area that is equal to the size of the trap door, which can be removed. Should the floor have been damaged whilst moving the stone, then the damaged area of the floor would be replaced. Look at the joists from the floor below and you can see the centre beam that would have been lifted out. A beam or girder would have been put across the trap door above and blocks and pulleys fixed to it. Bags of bran, eventually reaching to the ceiling, would have been piled underneath, as security against the stone dropping.

One of the present stones on the stone floor is dated 1853 and would have been made twenty five years after the mill had been opened. That this was an additional set of stones can be confirmed by looking at the beams on the Meal Floor,

You do not need to dress the Burr stones very often as they are harder than the barley stones. When we dressed the softer barley stones, usually twice each year, we put pulleys above and drove an iron bar between the stones before putting in wedges to open the stones further. A chain was put through the eye and the stone lifted, until it eventually stood on its edge. When it came time to lower the stone onto its back, then the chain was put through the eye in the opposite way. The chains had to be the correct way through the stone otherwise the operation wouldn't work correctly. We always had two men on hand in case of trouble during the few moments the stone stood on its edge without support.

Every part of the daily routine was important, but as my retirement came nearer my routine was very different from both my grandfather's and father's. They spent most of their time buying, selling and dealing with paperwork, not getting dusted up as I did by grinding corn for the farmers. We did not employ any clerical staff as Dad, after he had had his tea, worked from home in his office, until eight o'clock, every night to complete the paperwork and occasionally attending to his customers, and I did the same for all of my time as miller.

Fred would collect money from smallholders and, after he had had his tea, he would bring the money and the details to my father in his office at home.

Every Monday afternoon Frank Davison did not come into the mill but cycled around Whaplode, visiting farmers and the small stockholders, and those having a few chickens or a pig in their back garden. As he was secretary of the local British Legion, he would collect dues on this weekly journey as well as collecting orders for the animal feed and payment from those who had been out when their previous order had been delivered.

Most farm labourers had an allotment from the Parish Council, with a usual size of about an acre but sometimes, if the next plot was vacant, they would have the use of two plots. In wartime they grew crops that were easily saleable in small quantities. After the war they started to grow wheat with a yield of about two tons to the acre, contrasting with the present day yields of 4 tons plus per acre. As we started to take grain in bulk quantities, the growers would bring this grain directly into the yard. The contractors generally combined these small fields on bank holidays as the larger merchants were not open on those days, and then we were extra busy. During one August bank holiday, I took in one hundred tons of wheat with the help of farmers who were delivering grain.

When the sacks of grain were collected quickly (i.e. soon after the grain had been threshed), the farmer would have laid straw on the ground and stacked the sacks on top. We would arrive and the sacks were lifted onto the lorry using a sack winder. One man would have been given the job of working the sack winder, a continuous job, whilst the other men had short breaks whilst waiting to carry the next sack.

When the grain was stacked in a warehouse you would soon know its state because you only had to press the sack. If it was pliable then it was dry but if it was tight then it was wet. Even the big warehouses used this method in those days. When grain started to be stored in bulk the need for everything to be dry became more important.

In the early days if you had some wet grain from a stack roof then it would have been loaded on top in the railway trucks. A method which was common to all merchants was to include a wisp of straw in the tie, to mark it as containing wet grain. This would enable the wet corn to be mixed in with the dry at the end of the journey.

Before the war there wasn't enough English corn grown, so we used Russian or Canadian grain which was so dry you could tip some of each into the bins, one by one – English and foreign. As long as there was plenty of dry corn then a little damp wouldn't hurt. This method produces an even moisture content.

# Second World War

Wartime brought many changes to village and business life; evacuees, Home Guard, Air Raid Precaution (ARP) (later renamed Civil Defence), and food rationing to mention a few. First came the recruitment of ARP Wardens, who went around the village delivering gas masks and advising on their use. Next, on the outbreak of war, the evacuees arrived from Islington with their teachers and they used the classrooms, now the Village Hall, which were part of the Grammar School. Moulton Grammar School closed that very year and amalgamated with Spalding Grammar School. The evacuees were billeted with all the village families and became part of the community.

The Royal Army Medical Corps took over the main Grammar School buildings which contained classrooms and dormitories to be used as a field hospital had there been an invasion.

Following the Dunkirk evacuation, a company of the Queens Regiment was stationed in the village. They were quartered in the club rooms in the Swan Inn, the Axe and Handsaw, the Sports Pavilion and the Parish Room which was situated in Church Lane. A number of the soldiers slept in the Mill for a time, but I cannot remember the reason why. The redundant flour plant machinery was still in the warehouse/granary and the soldiers slept wherever they could find floor space between the machinery. A few of these soldiers married local girls and on their safe return settled in the village.

All this was very exciting for us boys. I was 11 years old at the time and starting my first term in September 1939 at Spalding

Grammar School. I used to travel to school by bus with my satchel over one shoulder and my gas mask over the other.

At the Mill, wartime brought its own changes and problems regarding how business was done. All grain trading was strictly controlled by the Ministry of Agriculture and all prices fixed. The price paid to the farmer, the merchant's margin and the price paid to the end user, whether for flour or animal feed, were all fixed. If we, as small merchants, sold to a middle merchant then the commission was divided between us. I believe that, at the time, the commission was two shillings a quarter so we each got one shilling (5p). There was an additional allowance for delivery to the railway of, I think, 2/- a quarter as most distant deliveries were then carried by train. Lorry fuel was scarce and rationed. There came a time when all wheat had to be sold for human consumption and farmers were not permitted to use wheat to feed their own livestock.

Feeding stuffs rationing was soon brought in, and coupons were issued to all livestock keepers, big and small, based on the number of animals kept at a certain date. This resulted in some who had reduced the number of stock receiving more than enough rations and those who wished to expand unable to obtain extra feed, causing some ill-feeling as it was illegal to swap or trade coupons. These coupons were given to your feed supplier who had to exchange them for permits at the local Food Office and then passed on to the larger mills who supplied compound feed. All of this caused a lot of office work, counting coupons, keeping a register of how many coupons each livestock keeper held etc. These coupons were issued monthly.

These days of food shortages encouraged many households to keep one or two pigs in their backyards and on application they received a monthly ration of 4 stones (25kg) of pig meal. If one belonged to a pig club, this ration was increased to 5 stones (31kg). As a result, most families who had a pig joined a pig club which had the added advantage that you were insured if unfortunately a pig died. When the pig came to be slaughtered, domestic bacon coupons for six months had to be surrendered in exchange for a permit to slaughter the pig. The animal would be taken to a local butcher or abattoir, or a travelling butcher who would kill and dress the pig on your premises. This was done in the winter months as there was little or no refrigeration then, and it was a common sight to see a pig carcass hanging from an apple tree.

These pigs were killed at a much much bigger weight than today. The pig was usually 25 stone live weight (160 kg), often over 30 stone (190 kg) or even 40 stone (250 kg) or more. This resulted in a lot of fat bacon and pork.

People gave pigs fries, small joints, sausages etc. to friends and neighbours who reciprocated when their own pig was killed. Pigs fry (also known as pork fry) is a traditional Lincolnshire meat dish featuring the cheaper but tastier parts of the pig. In the oldest versions, scraps of pork meat such as pork belly are mixed with various pieces of kidney, liver, heart, lights (lungs) and sweetbreads. Pigs fry can be cooked in a casserole or, as the name suggests, in a frying pan. Many traditional Lincolnshire butchers will sell it today, although some people tend to prefer it without as much offal. Many local butcher's standard offering has pieces of pork shoulder with kidney and liver. You can, of course, make up the pigs fry yourself – the mixture needs to be about 50% pork meat (e.g. belly, shoulder), with the remainder made up of various parts of offal. The pieces need to be bite-size around 3-4cm cubes or so.

The bacon and hams were cured at home in a salting tub which was a shallow tray about 4½ ft long by 2 ft wide by 6in deep often coated with pitch to avoid the brine escaping on to the pantry or outbuilding floor. Salt was obtained in dry blocks of about 2 stones in weight and had to be broken up into fine salt and rubbed onto the flitches of bacon which were then covered with loose salt and left for three weeks, being turned occasionally. Hams were similarly cured with the addition of some brown sugar resulting in a far superior taste compared with any you can buy today. After curing, the bacon and hams were dried by hanging from hooks in a warm dry place, often one's living room. When dried, they were sewn into muslin cloths and eaten later as required.

Lard was also made including some of the fat from the top of the sides of bacon taken off before curing and stored in jars.

Any of the remaining pieces of meat not suitable for joints etc. were rendered down to make brawn.

As you can see, in the words of the old saying, "everything from the pig was used except the squeal"

Backyard poultry keepers were allowed a small ration of feed called Balancer Meal to supplement their household scraps. This allowance was obtained by surrendering one's egg ration and was at the rate of 4lb (2kg) feed per ration book per month. Families and neighbours were allowed to band together in this scheme and share the eggs their hens laid. Each month we weighed 8 cwt (400kg) into small bags , the smallest being 4lb (one ration book) and the largest 32lb ready for delivery on our rounds. There were 105 of these customers in 1949.

In 1949 we had some 300 backyard pig keepers on our books from Moulton, Whaplode and Weston (Wragg Marsh). Pig and poultry keepers, and of course farmers, were looking to take delivery of their feed as soon as the new month started so we were extra busy for the first one or two weeks. We also had about the same number of farmers' customers with their own feed coupons who were professional farmers.

Feeding stuffs rationing finally came to an end in 1952.

During these times of food shortages, pig keeping was very profitable and many small farmers kept as many pigs as their rations and own grain would allow. These pigs were fed to bacon weight, 10 score (a score being 20lb) (90kg), live weight and then delivered to bacon factories in the Midlands. A Ministry of Food officer arranged this. One either got in touch with the officer direct or saw him at Spalding Corn Exchange which he attended most weeks. A local haulier, Slator Bros of Saracens Head, who had two livestock lorries delivered most of the pigs from this area.

At that time one could purchase a weaner pig at 8 weeks old from a breeder for £5, use £10 worth of feed to achieve bacon weight in about 12 weeks and the sale price was £20, a profit of £5 - the equivalent of a week's wages. Think what the price of bacon and pork would be today if the profit margin was a week's wage.

# John Biggadike III

## Transport and storage

I took over the Mill after the death of my father in 1964. I soon realised that in order to carry on I needed a larger lorry, some bulk storage and a means of drying grain. Bulk grain was becoming the way the business was going, and in order to store it successfully bulk grain was required to have a moisture content of 16% or less.

Until my father died in 1964 we never had any bulk storage. All the grain had to be delivered in sacks and 50 tons of grain could be stored on all the floors. Storage started from the second floor bin, which is now the archive room, and the floors above, in both bins and sacks. The sacks would be stacked so they stood 3 sacks high.

I purchased a new Bedford lorry with detachable high wooden sides to carry eight or nine tons and a small one-ton batch grain dryer. This dryer was heated by oil and was installed in the small shed adjoining the stables in which I had earlier kept pigs. With the help of one of my farmer cousins taking the early and late turns, we ran the dryer from 6am. until 11pm August to October, drying about 6 or 7 batches a day. During the first season, dried grain was weighed into 12-stone sacks and stored in the stables until being loaded on to the lorry for delivery to users. This now sounds amateurish, and I suppose it was, but these small dryers were very popular with farmers who wished to store their own grain.

The dryer was filled with grain by a portable grain auger, the lower end of which was put in a tin bath of the type many older people will remember. The bath was filled from the farm carts either from sacks or via a small trap door cut into the tailboard. Over the years, I acquired and used about 20 augers of varying lengths and capacities, and numerous tin baths because if farmers were at all careless drivers, the baths quickly became damaged beyond use.

As you can imagine, this system was not very satisfactory and before the next harvest, pits were installed in the yard so that farmers could tip a load more quickly. From the pit, grain was moved by conveyor into a holding bin in the shed and then onward to the dryer by augers. Likewise, a pit was dug under the dryer to hold a ton batch and conveyed by auger to the weighing machine. We then installed a bin in part of the stables with another auger through the wall.

All this was not sufficient due to the increasing amount of combine harvested grain, so in 1967, four 35-ton galvanised storage bins were installed in the yard. These were filled either by emptying sacks of grain which had been dried in the dryer, or directly by dry grain from the farm. This system soon proved inadequate and two of the bins had drying floors with an electric fan installed in them. Two further storage and drying bins were installed in a new building adjoining the mill granary. These held 30 tons each and enabled us to transfer bulk grain into the upper floor of the granary. The grain then had to be put into sacks so it could be used in the mill and this was unproductive work, but allowed us to remain in operation. At the maximum, we could store 300 tons of grain on the premises in bulk and in sacks.

At this time, many of my farmer customers liked to store their grain in sacks for sale later in the year and I supplied sacks for their use, knowing that I should be buying their grain later. In order to protect my stock of sacks from vermin damage, I purchased a redundant refrigerated lorry body which was mouse proof. At one point I was supplying these farmers with 5000 three-bushel sacks during the harvest period and all of these sacks had to be sorted, cleaned and repaired before the next harvest.

Before long, lorry weight restrictions were becoming much more tightly enforced and my Bedford lorry was not big enough. I replaced it with a Commer which I bought from a merchant friend of mine who replaced his lorries with new ones on a regular basis. This Commer was plated at 16 tons and so could carry a 10½ ton load. By this time, Moulton railway station had closed and the line had been shut, so all grain was transported by road. We tried to do our own deliveries whenever possible, resorting to a haulage contractor only if the distance involved was too great.

In order to carry bigger legal loads, wooden lorry bodies were being superseded by lightweight alloy ones, so when in 1976 the chance came, I bought a Seddon lorry which served us well for several years. I sold this lorry to a local farmer who also did haulage and he was a great help with deliveries later on when business had declined and I no longer ran my own vehicle. My last lorry was a Ford, capable of carrying 16 tons, but its purchase was an unsuccessful attempt to remain competitive because I did not have sufficient business to keep this lorry in full-time work.

In those days, we used to deliver loads of wheat right into Yorkshire, Manchester and all over the place. We were continually being out-classed due to the increasing lorry capacity. We were struggling but it was the only way to carry on.

I also purchased a small truck carrying 1 ton to be used for local deliveries of feed etc., which I later replaced with one carrying 1½ tons . In my last few years at the mill, I carried out most of these smaller deliveries myself.

All these ways of dealing in grain have now been overtaken as farmers now have large buildings with drying floors on the level and grain is moved by bucket loaders, carrying at least at ton at a time, mounted on tractors.

## Milling Miscellany

On his one of his periodic visits the factory inspector stated that we needed a method of alerting people to a fire. We acquired a piece of scrap steel from Pettit's and this was hung up near the stairs and is still there today. We used a large spanner to strike it and this satisfied the inspector's requirements at the time.

The large ladder hanging on the upstairs granary wall and covered in hanging sacks is a ricking ladder. The building had been partly slated and the wind had started to blow off the slates. I bought this long ladder for about £7 at a farm sale. Its proper use was that for stacking corn and being used as a thatching ladder against high corn ricks.

There is little trace of the sails that were removed in 1895 but what remained was stored under one of the trees until I made use of it for my poultry houses. When the mill restoration had started and as I had retired, the timber was returned, as I thought it was a bit of mill history.

One other aspect of life at the mill was the habit of a number of local farmers to meet in the Mill, particularly on a wet day, to chat about farming, the weather etc. and generally put the world to rights.

The only reason I hadn't applied to the Guinness Book of Records for an entry as the tallest mill in England was because I couldn't operate the business as well as taking people round the mill. If anyone came enquiring then I let them wander on their own round the mill, after I had warned them to be careful. You trusted them to act in a sensible way as in the main they were mill enthusiasts.

In my youth, there were 12 similar businesses within a six-mile radius of Moulton, all individually owned and run by their owners. Many of these were much larger businesses than ours, but I continued in business longer than any of them.

In about 1948/50 the floor on the second floor began to dip very slightly due to the extra weight of grain being stored on the floor above, sufficiently to hinder the complete opening of the office door. A steel support was added to the floor with a concrete base in the cellar inscribed with my father's initials and the date.

One of our suppliers, Pauls of Kings Lynn, produced a flaked maize, known as Kositos, which was twice as big as a cornflake. We sold this mixed with cows, horses and pigs rations.

Sacks of grain were heavy, weighing up to 18 stone (115kg) if the moisture content was average and so three helping hands are described:-

1. Lorries were later fitted with a mechanical lifting device on their rear to help the lorry man manoeuvre the heavy sacks of grain. The 'Shoulder-High' consisted of a hydraulic ram attached to the back of the lorry. On arrival at the farm a long cradle was attached to the ram and the other end rested on the ground. The employee tipped the sack of grain upside-down on the cradle, which tightened the belt, causing the ram to raise the cradle containing the sack of grain, vertically in the air and level to the shoulder height of the worker. The loader would then take the sack off the 'Shoulder-High' and with the sack on his shoulder could then walk along the bed of the lorry. This device saved the use of a man manipulating a sack winding truck, or the lorry driver having to climb a ladder carrying the sack on his back.

2. When moving full-sized sacks in the mill, an ordinary sack barrow was used. When a sack was to be put on the top of another sack, a sack winder barrow, which had a winding gear on one side, was used, to raise the sack to a comfortable height. For smaller sacks a hicking stick could be used.

3. A 'Hicking stick' was a simple labour-saving tool that had been available for a long time and used when lifting heavy loads. This was a strong, round stick, often the shaft of a fork and about a metre in length. Two men would each hold one end of the stick and it would act as a pivot to the sack.

The hicking stick would be placed against the base of the sack and the free hand would heave the sack against the hicking stick, so jerking it onto the bed of the lorry.

This device was used by farmers to help when lifting 8 stone (50kg) sacks of potatoes or corn. When the sack was in the air one man would release his end of the hicking stick and the sack of potatoes would be swung onto his shoulder. The pair of them would continue this for some time until the stack of potato sacks had been transferred onto the lorry. If there was a dyke between the clamp and the lorry then the sacks would have been hicked onto a man's back and walked across the bridge over the dyke. 'Tati graves' was the local name for a potato clamp.

To hick-      hoist, hitch, jerk

'hickings wortse than carrying'.

'he broke his body wi' hicking corn'.

So 'hicking barrow' the barrow or cratch by which a sack of corn is hicked or hoisted on to a man's back.

Taken from 'A glossary of words used in South Lincolnshire'' - 1896

## Replacing the Cap Cover
The original Ogee cap on the Mill was replaced in 1928 by the galvanised iron cap which was there until the restoration. It was installed by a local tradesman, Zac Baxter, who I understand was disabled with a club foot. He completed the task without scaffolding using a platform through the putlock holes in the Mill and turning the top as necessary. The new cap

was built on the turntable so the top could be turned and was constructed using wood covered by galvanised iron.

Over the years the galvanised iron became rusted and deteriorated and in 1971, our local village carpenter Fount Hemmant suggested that he would be willing to undertake the removal of the rusted iron and replacing it with new. We obtained the necessary materials and painted the iron before we used it. We then proceeded to take off two sections of the roof, which luckily was not tongue and grooved and, working one section at a time, recovered and replaced the roof ending at the trapdoor.

The sides presented a bigger challenge as they were 4ft 6in high, so although we had predrilled the necessary holes, the far corner was almost out of reach. Fount overcame this by holding the nail with a piece of wire and leaning over and hitting it with a hammer while I held on to him.

Fortunately this was in the days before Health and Safety regulations. It was all undertaken with great care and was a most enjoyable and interesting task completed by the three of us: Fount, his workman Clifford Clark and myself.

I used to open the trapdoor on national occasions and taking a ladder place the Union Flag on the Mill knob. The last such occasion was after I had left the mill together with Byron Hahn to celebrate the Millenium.

### Changes in Farming
When horses were the prime source of power, a mill supplied power to the land but after the war the business started to reduce as the number of horses had started to decline with the

introduction of tractors. When the horses went, as tractors were purchased, then that part of our business also went.

Competition was increasing and the bigger milling companies and corn merchants began to target our trade. We bought from these larger concerns the products we did not produce ourselves. Previously, they did not have contact with the local farmers as there were few telephones or representatives calling at the farms. Slowly they started to take our business, especially with the larger farmers. We still bought feed from them as our smaller farmers had to be supplied.

Whenever a small farmer retired, his land was taken over by one of his neighbours so increasing their acreage to cover the cost of the ever increasing price and capacity of the new equipment. This had the effect of finishing the small merchant and the small farmer who had been the backbone of the business for many generations, and made it very much more difficult for the younger generation to get a start in farming.

# Retirement and the Mill

My wife, Maureen, and I were married in 1972 and enjoyed 34 years of happy marriage until her death in 2006. She had been a secretary in the office of one of the local milling firms. Although she was not of an agricultural background, she enjoyed working among the poultry, cattle, pigs and sheep that we kept on the three acres of land adjoining our house on Broad Lane. Her favourites were the pigs.

During the latter days of the mill, I only had a part-time workman in. On the days when he was not available and I had to go out delivering feed, seed corn etc., Maureen took over serving the customers and she enjoyed their conversation while doing so. She would fill in any spare time by weighing wheat into 25kg retail sacks

As she was a good knitter with something always on her needles, she occupied her time there.

All this became very trying as we looked for a way to dispose of the premises and ensure the future of the mill.

I was approaching the age of sixty and it was too late to think of doing anything else, so I decided to carry on until my retirement, despite the business making a very small profit margin.

I had looked forward to the business closing in 1990, which would have been 100 years after my Grandfather had started the business in Whaplode. Due to circumstances I had to continue for another five years. Throughout this time the business continued in a small way but gradually was reduced. I stopped buying the farmers' grain, except for a small quantity to fill the bins to enable me to sell on later in the year.

In the meantime we ran the mill down but nothing seemed to happen. I could not go on any longer on my own so I closed the business in 1995. The premises were my own, but if I had had to pay rent the finances would have been difficult. During my years in business I had amongst my farmer customers many whose parents and even grandparents had traded with us over the years and whose loyalty enabled me to carry on in those last difficult years. After such a long association we all became, and still are, very good friends which I greatly appreciate.

In 1988, it came to my notice that John Van Geest was applying for planning permission to build houses on his factory site next door so I contacted the estate agent and told him that he could include the mill field in with their application for planning permission as it could have access off the big estate. By the time that planning permission had come through the housing boom was over. Mr. John Van Geest sold the factory next to the mill to Gardmans who transferred their distribution Centre and offices for their gardening enterprise from Pinchbeck

I later tried various schemes including one that the land might be sold for housing. Plans were drawn up for quality housing but South Holland District Council, planning department would not hear of the land being developed until the future of the mill had been secured. The Council asked what I was going to do with the mill and how was I going to deal with it, as it was grade one listed.

Broadgate Homes was the only company that had ever shown

an interest in the premises. David Clarke, the Managing Director, had worked on a few listed buildings and this one had started to intrigue him, as we negotiated together. I give David full credit for his part in the final outcome. He said he wanted to do something with the site and kept his word despite the many difficulties. A plan at the time was to put the mill tower into a charity, convert the warehouse into offices, which they would let, with the field to be used for building. We formed three companies to enable us to achieve these plans and they had wanted me to be part of these companies, as I might have helped them to achieve the application for planning permission, but this was not acceptable to the planning authorities. Broadgate Homes and their Housing Association partners were in regular contact with the council and in the early 90's the planning department had suggested to them that the land might be suitable for affordable housing. Plans were suggested for sixteen dwellings in several blocks but this plan understandably generated a significant number of objections and was refused. Under no circumstances would they tell me what they wanted; their response was that it was up to the applicant to put in plans to the Council.

A question was asked by the planning department at one point regarding how I intended to ensure the upkeep of the mill after my death, as it was Grade One listed. I had got it, I was responsible for it and I was stuck with it! This was a very unpleasant situation to be in.

Plans for a care home were then suggested by Broadgate Homes as one of their subsidiary companies, Abbeygate, already had one in Crowland. I had already agreed a price for the land with them, but as yet there had been no additional provision for payment for the mill - this would have depended on the use to which it might have been put. English Heritage were consulted and they involved the Lincolnshire Mills Group.

There were numerous meetings held without making progress and I remember one meeting with English Heritage and several members of the Lincolnshire Mills Group where everyone had become very exasperated. During this meeting I said that if I were able to give the mill to the Mills Group would they accept it? They had thought that this was a wonderful idea, which was eventually to become a step in the eventual outcome.

English Heritage found faults with the proposals although we were all trying to achieve the same result and they were not in favour of building behind the mill as they said it would block the view. That side of the mill is covered by fields where no one would go to get a view of the mill, the only roads where it can be viewed from is Eastgate and Cobgate. As has now been proved by experience, a single storey building has little visual impact at that distance.

The many meetings meant that my legal bill continued to increase. There came a time for another meeting at the Council Offices with representatives from English Heritage, the Council, Lincolnshire Mills Group, and Broadgate Homes. I decided not to go to the meeting but I was represented by my solicitor who didn't contact me for two days. Eventually he telephoned me and said that he had been giving consideration to the next step as he had to report there had been little progress. It had always been the case that I had wanted the mill to be, at least preserved, or better, restored. David Clarke put forward the suggestion that Broadgate Homes would take all of the property and leave me out of the discussions. My solicitor had thought that I had wanted to be involved and this idea would have been unacceptable to me. I asked him to repeat what he had just said. He did repeat what he had said and I responded by telling him not to waste any time and to get onto it that day. There had been no price mentioned for the mill buildings.

Broadgates's solicitors were soon contacted and the matter progressed. There was always the possibility that Broadgate Homes might back out due to all the complications, but David Clarke was as good as his word. By that time the plans for the care home had been discussed with the council. David Clarke came to finalise the details and we had finally reached the stage of getting a provisional contract in place. He did not increase the price that he had already offered for the land, but I did not expect he would.

There was no payment included for the mill buildings, not even the proverbial pound, as it was part and parcel of one deal.

I don't know what the position would have been had I not dealt with Broadgate Homes. The only thing I could see at the time was to put the mill into a limited company and abandon it.

In due course work started on the care home and it was decided to hold a public meeting together with the Lincolnshire Mills Group, with the aim of looking for a way forward. This group are an advisory group so have little money. They decided to start up a restoration project and called a village meeting. A proposal to create a Charitable Company was accepted to undertake the restoration with Janet Prescott as the secretary and Byron Hahn, who had recently moved into the village, as chairman.

A board of directors was formed by the charitable company, including a member from the Lincolnshire Mills Group. Broadgate Homes passed over the lease for a period of two hundred years, at a peppercorn rent of a pound a year, with Broadgate Homes retaining the freehold. This was paid by Thomas Stoten, the Lord of the Manor of Moulton Bewsolas,

The village miller had been the same for hundreds of years but times and circumstances had changed, making the story of commercial milling in Moulton, started in at least 1237, seemingly come to an end.

However, this is not the end of the story of Moulton Windmill. In 1986, Peter Dolman wrote a review about all the Lincolnshire mills and under his entry for this mill he had said "that if any mill was worth restoring then it was Moulton, but would it ever be done?". The success of the Windmill Project has exceeded all expectations. It has resulted in the full restoration and the mill is now a tourist attraction, being the tallest and finest windmill in the country, producing flour and visited by thousands of people. How this has been achieved is a story for someone else to tell.

All I can say is that after many difficulties the outlook for the mill now seems secure for the foreseeable future and no one could be more pleased than I am with the final outcome.

## ACKNOWLEDGEMENTS

There are, inevitably, lots of people without whom this book would never have been completed. Here are some of them:

The King family, Lincs Free Press, Mr E Crampton, Mr A Inkley and Jane Cooke for one of more photographs each.

The directors of Moulton Windmill Projects for their unstinting support.

The late Jim Critchley for getting the book started and leaving all the research.

John Biggadike for the stories and the many happy hours spent in his company.

My son James who proof read the draft. All errors are mine.

My wife, Jini for her forebearance.

Peter Hall, Oct 2014

## APPENDICES

Appendix A - The King Family Tree

Appendix B - An extract from Lincolnshire Windmills; Contemporary Survey', by Peter C. Dolman published by Lincolnshire Library Service, 1986

# The King Family Tree

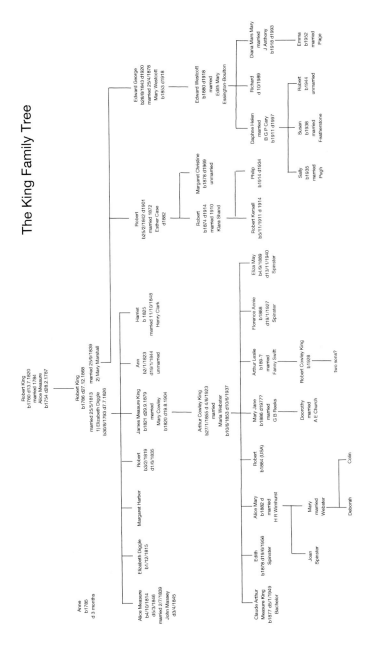

An extract from Lincolnshire Windmills; Contemporary Survey', by Peter C. Dolman published by Lincolnshire Library Service, 1986 - ISBN 0861111265

Moulton TF307240 1972, 1977 int., 1982 int.

This colossal tower has the distinction of being the largest surviving windmill not only in Lincolnshire, but in the whole country. It cannot claim to be the largest complete windmill, that honour falling to Sutton mill in Norfolk, which is 80ft. high to the top of its cap. Moulton mill is however is 80 feet high to the top of the kerb and was originally about 97 feet to the top of its ogee cap. It was built in about 1822 by Robert King. The sails were removed in 1895 after gale damage, when a steam mill with a two sack Turner roller milling plant was installed in the adjoining granary, steam power also being applied to the original stones. Serious milling ceased many years ago although a small roller mill and kibbler probably see occasional use. The main use of the mill is as a store in connection with the grain merchant's business of Mr . Biggadike, whose family have owned the Mill since 1924.

[Note:- this is not actually true. The Biggadike family operated the mill from 1924, but did not acquire it until 1951]

The tower is 28 feet 9 inches in diameter at ground level and 12 feet diameter at the kerb, both internally. The basement contains the engine drive gearing which then ascends to the great spur wheel by way of a vertical shaft. the elevated ground floor is spacious enough to contain a proper partitioned miller's office. The first floor contains a Turner "Inkoos" mill and kibbler and Hunt's roller mill, both electrically powered. The second floor has large storage bins. The third floor was the spout floor; unfortunately the governor has gone. Access the reefing stage , now missing, was formerly at this level; the two door openings have been partly bricked up. The three pairs of stones are on the fourth floor. Two pairs of french stones remain in place with their vats; one pair are 4'6" and one pair are 4'4", the latter having the plate around the eye "W.J. & CHILD MAKER.HULL.1853". The pair of grey stones are 4stones are 4'8" diameter, and have been taken up, now leaning against the wall.

The spur gearing differs from the usual Lincolnshire pattern in that the stone nuts are all iron, the great spur wheel having morticed wooden cogs. This arrangement is fine until a breakage when the job of recogging would take several weeks. The spur wheel has an iron hub and rim with eight radial wooden spokes. the cogs are of very fine pitch and are very wide, which must have given a smooth drive. The engine drive engages the spur wheel by means of another small iron nut. The nuts are 12 inches in diameter and the great spur wheel is 8'9" in diameter.

The fifth and sixth floors both contain bins, the seventh is empty and eighth is the dust floor. The Wallower is an impressive wooden clasp-arm bevel wheel of about 6 feet in diameter with wooden cogs. A friction rim on the underside formerly drove the endless chain sackhoist, now displaced in favour of an electric hoist. The upright shaft is of wood and is 14 inches square. It changes to iron 5½ inches diameter just above the spur wheel.

The kerb is a hexagonal wooden frame built into the

brickwork, with an iron track and an inward facing tooth ring beneath which the centering wheel run. The cap frame is in poor condition, but survives mostly intact apart from where the sheertrees have been cut off beyond the new roof(fitted in 1928 to replace the old ogee cap). The windshaft has gone but the tail bearing housing remains, as does the hand winding gear. Parts of the brake wheel also remain in the basement.

The mill had four double sided patent sails, which unusually for Lincolnshire were carried on stocks in a poll end. The fanstage was of typical local type with the rear fly posts almost vertical. Apart from the loss of its windshaft and original roof, the mill is remarkably complete and is well cared for at present. It is certainly a viable candidate for full restoration, but whether or not this can be achieved remains to be seen.